# SETTING SAIL

S0-BEZ-504

Can you number these pictures to show what
happened first, second, and so on?

Illustrated by Charles Jordan

Answer on page 47.

# COMMON SENSE

Study the pictures in each group and figure out what they have in common. The answers may not always be easy to "see," but they will make sense.

1.

2.

3.

4.

5.

Illustrated by Jerry Zimmerman

# MUSICAL CHAIRS

How many differences can you spot between these two scenes?

# BAFFLING BOXES

Start in the middle to work your way through these boxes.

FINISH

Answer on page 47.

# THE CLEAN-UP BRIGADE

You'll clean up this mess of letters by finding the 23 hidden words. Look up, down, across, backward, and diagonally. Some letters will appear in more than one word. When you've found all the words, the leftover letters will spell out how you look.

| | |
|---|---|
| Brush | Robe |
| Bubbles | Scrub |
| Care | Sink |
| Comb | Slippers |
| Face | Soap |
| Floss | Suds |
| Hair | Tap |
| Hands | Teeth |
| Lather | Towel |
| Powder | Tub |
| Rinse | Washcloth |
| | Water |

Illustrated by Anni Matsick

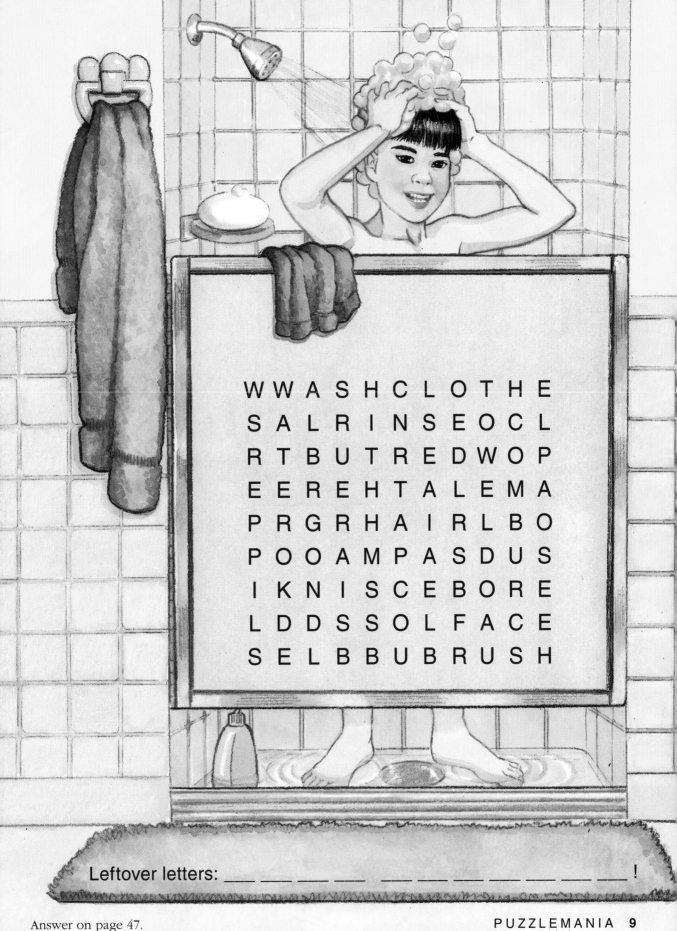

W W A S H C L O T H E
S A L R I N S E O C L
R T B U T R E D W O P
E E R E H T A L E M A
P R G R H A I R L B O
P O O A M P A S D U S
I K N I S C E B O R E
L D D S S O L F A C E
S E L B B U B R U S H

Leftover letters: \_\_ \_\_ \_\_ \_\_ \_\_ \_\_ \_\_ \_\_ \_\_ \_\_ \_\_ \_\_ \_\_ \_\_ !

# MULTIPLYING RABBITS

Solve each of the multiplication problems. Then write the letter in the matching numbered spaces to find the names of eight famous rabbits.

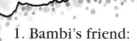

4 x 6 = ___ (A)

3 x 7 = ___ (H)  2 x 3 = ___ (U)  9 x 7 = ___ (Y)

2 x 1 = ___ (P)  2 x 5 = ___ (B)  1 x 8 = ___ (C)

5 x 4 = ___ (I)  6 x 3 = ___ (E)  4 x 4 = ___ (G)

5 x 3 = ___ (S)  8 x 5 = ___ (R)  7 x 5 = ___ (T)

7 x 8 = ___ (M)  8 x 4 = ___ (N)  2 x 2 = ___ (O)

1. Bambi's friend:

    ___ ___ ___ ___ ___ ___ ___
    35  21  6  56  2  18  40

2. Pooh's pal:

    ___ ___ ___ ___ ___ ___
    40  24  10  10  20  35

3. Wonderland inhabitant:

    ___ ___ ___ ___ ___ ___ ___ ___ ___
    56  24  40  8  21   21  24  40  18

4. Egg deliverer:

    ___ ___ ___ ___ ___ ___ ___ ___ ___ ___ ___
    18  24  15  35  18  40   10  6  32  32  63

5. Beatrix Potter's bunny:

    ___ ___ ___ ___ ___ ___ ___ ___ ___ ___
    2  18  35  18  40   40  24  10  10  20  35

6. Elmer's enemy:

    ___ ___ ___ ___ ___ ___ ___ ___ ___
    10  6  16  15   10  6  32  32  63

7. Uncle Remus hero:

    ___ ___ ___ ___ ___ ___ ___ ___ ___
    10  40  18  40   40  24  10  10  20  35

8. Jessica's husband:

    ___ ___ ___ ___ ___ ___ ___ ___ ___ ___
    40  4  16  18  40   40  24  10  10  20  35

Answer on page 47.

# MAILBOX MEMORIES

## Part 1

Take a long look at this picture. Try to remember everything you see in it. Then turn the page, and try to answer some questions about it without looking back.

Illustrated by John Nez

DON'T READ THIS UNTIL YOU HAVE LOOKED AT "Mailbox Memories—Part I" ON PAGE 11.

# MAILBOX MEMORIES Part II

Can you answer these questions about the mailbox scene you saw? Don't peek!

1. Where did Mary live?
2. What was the name of the local newspaper?
3. What letter was atop the barn's wind vane?
4. What symbol was on the button on Mary's hat?
5. What color were Mary's sneakers?
6. How many bees were in the scene?
7. How many other animals were in the scene?
8. Was Mary mailing or receiving the letter in her hand?
9. Was Mary wearing earrings?
10. How many stripes were on Mary's shirt?

Answer on page 47.

# SHE SAVES SEASHELLS

Tiffany collects seashells during the months that have no "R" in the spelling of their names. If she collects one shell each day during those months, how many shells will she collect in one year?

Answer on page 47.

# DOT MAGIC

Join these dots from 1 to 78 to find a famous landmark.

# HIDDEN PICTURES

There are at least 17 objects hidden
in this picture. How many can you find?

Illustrated by Maurie Jo Manning

# WORD PAIRS

Two shorter but related words are hidden
in each pair of words given below.

For example: moment, doodad.

You can find MOM and DAD hiding in these two
words. Can you now find the other hidden pairs?

1.
struck, cargo

2.
scatter, doggerel

3.
vacant, ajar

4.
charm, legion

5.
kitchen, auburn

6.
gold, agent

7.
badger, good-bye

8.
going, shout

9.
history, sherbet

10.
cribbage, bedazzle

11.
farmer, branch

12.
grunt, fasten

Answer on page 47.

# LAST GAS

Today, Chester's Gas Station had five customers (including Vickers). Each of the five were driving a different type of vehicle (one person drove an 18-wheeler semi) and stopped at the gas station for a different reason. From the information provided, determine the name of each person driving each type of vehicle, and what each person stopped for (one stopped to put water in his/her radiator).

Use the chart to keep track of your answers. Put an "X" in each box that can't be true and a "O" in the box where information matches. For example, read clue 1. You can now put an X in all the boxes that don't match with Mr. Wells.

| | | Vehicle | | | | | Reason for stopping | | | | |
|---|---|---|---|---|---|---|---|---|---|---|---|
| | | motorcycle | sedan | semi-truck | station wagon | van | air | bathroom | gasoline | oil | water |
| Person | Stuart | | | | | | | | | | |
| | Taylor | | | | | | | | | | |
| | Vickers | | | | | | | | | | |
| | Wells | | | | | | | | | | |
| | Zuna | | | | | | | | | | |
| Reason for stopping | air | | | | | | | | | | |
| | bathroom | | | | | | | | | | |
| | gasoline | | | | | | | | | | |
| | oil | | | | | | | | | | |
| | water | | | | | | | | | | |

1. Mr. Wells, who was driving neither the sedan nor the semi-truck, did not stop for gas or oil.

2. The person driving the station wagon stopped to put air in a low tire.

3. Ms. Stuart and the driver of the motorcycle (who is not Zuna) stopped, in no particular order, for water and to use the bathroom.

4. Mr. Vickers, who was driving the van, did not stop to buy oil.

5. Taylor and Zuna, in no particular order, drove the semi-truck and stopped for water.

Answer on page 48.

# IN THE KITCHEN

Use the clues to fill in the grid.

## Across

1. Aluminum or tin _____
3. Cooked in oven
7. You and me
8. _____ the table.
9. Leave
10. Edgar Allan _____
11. Time past
12. Put things on this inside the cabinet
14. Freezer makes it
15. French _____
18. What happened when you peeled onions
20. Frying _____
22. Bar or pole
23. Exists
24. Sack
25. Cry of pain
26. Was carried off
27. Place for meals and lodging

## Down

1. Mugs
2. Sweet _____ sugar
3. Kind of meat
4. Preposition refers to place or time
5. Comes from a chicken
6. Open this and walk in.
8. Filet of _____, type of fish
10. Nut used to make pies
11. Sharp, bitter taste or smell
13. Hello
15. Toad's relative
16. Old-fashioned you
17. Rod for cooking meat over fire
18. _____berry
19. Not up
21. As happy _____ __ lark (2 words)
24. Exist
25. Not off

JORDAN

Answer on page 48.

19

# ROW, ROW, ROW

Each timepiece has something in common with the two others in
the same row. For example, in the top row across, each timepiece
is digital. Look at the other rows across, down, and diagonally.
What's the same about each row of three?

Illustrated by Rich Johnson

Answer on page 48.

# STOP, LOOK, AND LIST

For each category below, try to name three
things that begin with the letter "F."

## THINGS IN A SWIMMING POOL

_____

_____

_____

## THINGS TO EAT

_____

_____

_____

## HOT WORDS

_____

_____

_____

## NUMBERS

_____

_____

_____

Illustrated by Lisa Dayer

Answer on page 48.

# PICTURE MIXER

Copy these mixed-up squares in the spaces on the next page to put this picture back together. The letters and numbers tell you where each square belongs. The first one, A-3, has been done for you.

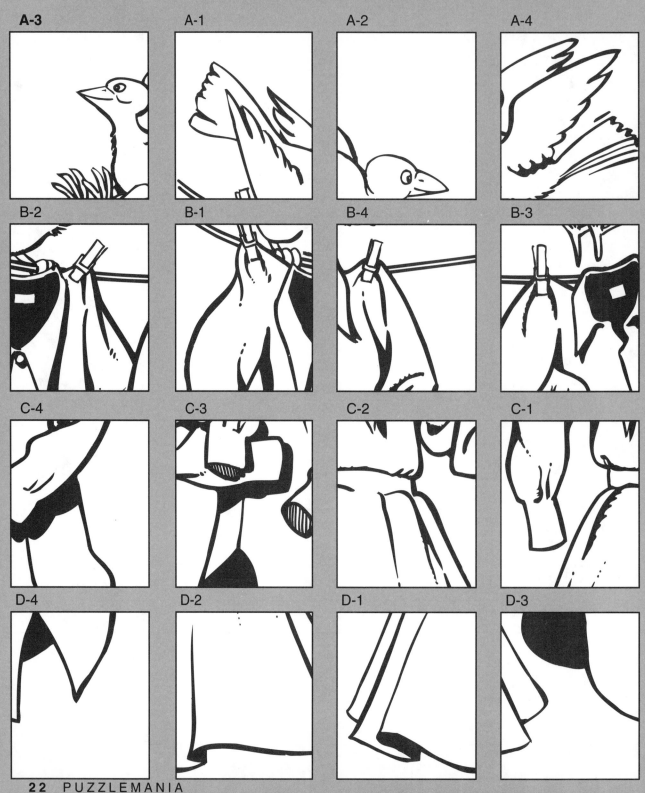

|  | 1 | 2 | 3 | 4 |
|---|---|---|---|---|
| A |  |  |  |  |
| B |  |  |  |  |
| C |  |  |  |  |
| D |  |  |  |  |

# TALL TALE TOOLS

These heroes are all missing their tools.
Fix the problem by matching them with
the proper equipment.

Paul Bunyan

John
Henry

Johnny
Appleseed

Casey Jones

Pecos Bill

Mike Fink

Illustrated by Marc Nadel

Answer on page 48.

# WHAT'S IN A WORD?

Flowers and trees come out during springtime. But there are also a lot of words hidden in the letters of SPRINGTIME. How many words of three letters or more can you bring into bloom?

_____    _____

_____    _____

_____    _____

_____    _____

_____

_____

_____

_____

Answer on page 48.

Illustrated by Anni Matsick

# MONKEYING AROUND

Stop making faces and look over here. Each of these 20 monkeys, apes, and primates can be put into this grid in one unique way. Use the size of each word as a clue to where it might fit. Words in parentheses do not go in the puzzle.

**3 Letters**
APE

**4 Letters**
SAKI

**5 Letters**
BLACK (ape)
LEMUR
LORIS
POTTO
(tree) SHREW

**6 Letters**
AYE-AYE
MONKEY
RHESUS
SPIDER (monkey)

**7 Letters**
GORILLA
MACAQUE
SAPAJOU
TAMARIN

**8 Letters**
MANDRILL
MARMOSET

**9 Letters**
ORANGUTAN
RED UAKARI

**10 Letters**
GOLDEN LION (tamarin)

Answer on page 49.

# WHEEL PROBLEMS

How many unusual things can you see in this picture?

# INSTANT PICTURE

Something is gliding across this water. To see what it is,
fill in each space that contains two dots.

Illustrated by Rob Sepanak

Answer on page 49.

# GLOBE PROBE

That intrepid explorer, Cincinnati Holmes, has always believed in being a good neighbor. For example, he knows that Canada and Mexico are two neighbors of the United States of America. He's shown six countries and listed some neighbors of each. If you can find the neighbors, you should be able to tell the country.

1. Iraq, Afghanistan, Pakistan

_____

2. Peru, Brazil, Chile

_____

3. Mali, Libya

_____

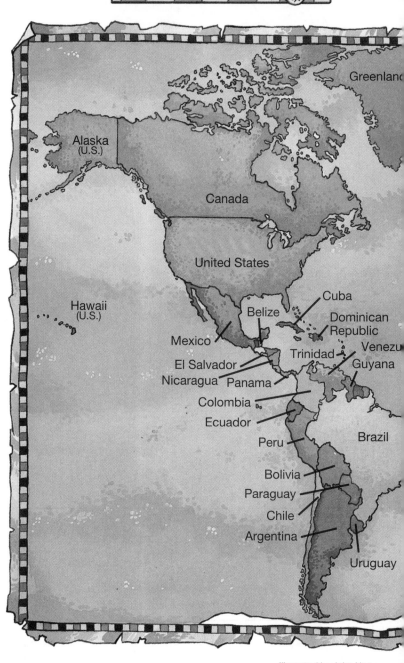

Greenland

Alaska (U.S.)

Canada

United States

Hawaii (U.S.)

Cuba
Belize
Dominican Republic
Mexico
Trinidad
Venezu
El Salvador
Guyana
Nicaragua  Panama
Colombia
Ecuador
Peru
Brazil
Bolivia
Paraguay
Chile
Argentina
Uruguay

Illustrated by John Nez

**4. Namibia, South Africa**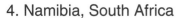

**5. Germany, Spain**

**6. Myanmar, Laos**

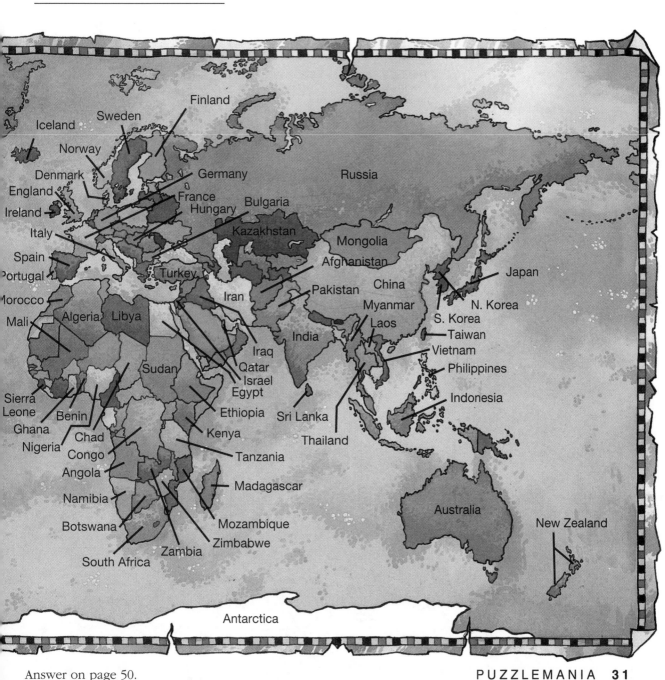

Finland

Iceland

Sweden

Norway

Denmark

England

Ireland

Germany

France

Hungary

Bulgaria

Russia

Italy

Kazakhstan

Spain

Mongolia

Portugal

Afghanistan

Turkey

Morocco

Iran

Pakistan

China

Japan

Mali

Algeria  Libya

Myanmar

N. Korea

S. Korea

India

Laos

Taiwan

Iraq

Vietnam

Sudan

Qatar

Israel

Egypt

Philippines

Sierra
Leone

Benin

Ethiopia

Sri Lanka

Indonesia

Ghana

Chad

Kenya

Thailand

Nigeria

Congo

Tanzania

Angola

Madagascar

Namibia

Australia

Botswana

New Zealand

Mozambique

Zimbabwe

Zambia

South Africa

Antarctica

# WATT AN IDEA!

There are at least 21 lightbulbs in this scene. How many do you see?

Illustrated by Joe Boddy

# TROUBLE ON THE LINE

Can you tell who's hooked up
to each machine?

# DAZE OF THE MONTH

This calendar page may look silly, but it holds the answer to a very important riddle. Follow the clues from date to date to find the letters mentioned. Put the letters into the spaces whose number matches each statement, and you'll come up with the answer in no time.

- October 32nd holds the ninth letter.
- Find letter four on the second Thursday.
- Smash Wednesday will give you letter one.
- Letter five is featured on the day of the afternoon solstice.
- Harbor Day has letter six.
- The third Tuesday after the second Monday has letter ten.
- St. Hat Trick's Day, honoring the hockey player who chased all the snakes out of Madison Square Garden, has letter seven.
- The date of the blue moon holds letter two.
- Letter eight can be found on Garbage Day.
- Dependence Day will give you letter three.

## Why are Saturday and Sunday so limp?

___ ___ ___ ___ ___, ___ ___ ___ ___ ___ ___ ___ ___ ___ ___ ___ ___ ___ .
　1　 2　 3　 4　 5　 3　　1　 2　 3　　6　 3　 3　 7　　3　 8　 9　10

Illustrated by Susanne Demarco

# ORDER IN THE COIN ROOM

There is a perfectly logical arrangement in the order of each of the rows of coins shown below. For example, in row one the coins are arranged in order of monetary value from least to most. Can you identify the scheme of arrangement for the other rows?

**1.**

**2.**

**3.**

Illustrated by Marc Nadel

**4.**

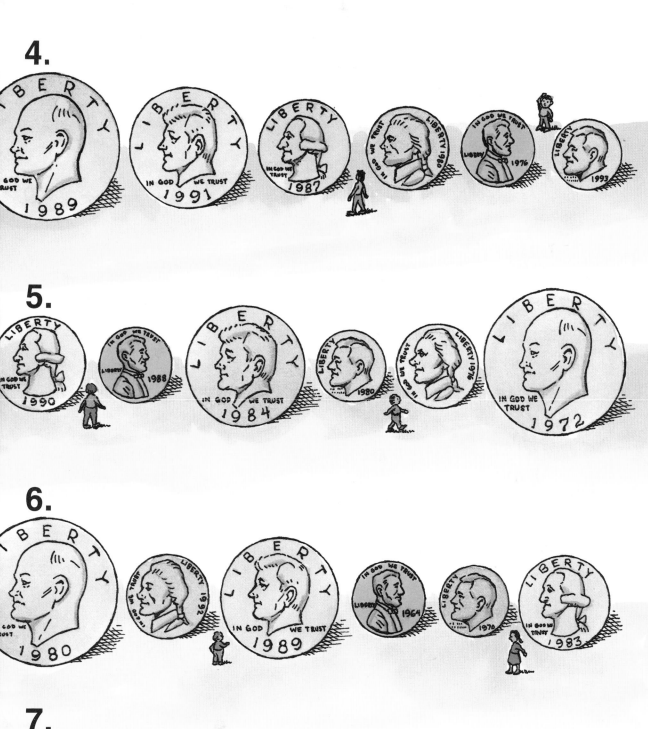

**5.**

**6.**

**7.**

# BIG AL

Our friend AL appears at the end of all these words.
Use the definitions as clues to fill in the rest of each word.

1. Actual, true: _____ _____ AL
2. Sleek marine mammal: _____ _____ AL
3. To give out cards in a game: _____ _____ AL
4. Take without paying or permission: _____ _____ _____ AL
5. Part of a flower: _____ _____ AL
6. Sea animals whose skeletons form reefs: _____ _____ AL
7. Meaning to a fable or story: _____ _____ AL
8. Hairy animal that feeds milk to its young: _____ _____ _____ AL
9. Of the mind: _____ _____ _____ _____ AL
10. Breakfast food made from grain: _____ _____ _____ _____ AL
11. Radio or TV antenna: _____ _____ _____ _____ AL
12. More than a couple, less than a dozen: _____ _____ _____ _____ AL
13. Crested red bird: _____ _____ _____ _____ _____ AL
14. Describing the fall season: _____ _____ _____ _____ _____ AL

Illustrated by Barbara Gray

Answer on page 49.

# HIGH FLYER

What is at the end of Jose's kite string?
Is it a boxed beauty or a bat bomber?
Use your imagination and draw in a
terrific kite.

Illustrated by Terry Kovalcik

# WONDERS DOWN UNDER

No, this puzzle is not about Australia. It's about things that are found underground. Each of the numbers below stands for a letter of the alphabet. Use the code to identify these underground things. To get you started, the code numbers for each letter in WONDERS DOWN UNDER are given below.

W=3  O=2  N=4  D=1  E=6  R=7  S=9  U=5

2-8-1   1-2-21   26-2-4-6-9

3-2-7-17-9

14-6-11-4-5-16-9

26-5-7-19-6-1   16-7-6-11-9-5-7-6

17-2-8-6-9

Illustrated by Dominic Catalano

13-2-9-9-19-8-9

11-4-16  18-2-8-2-4-19-6-9

14-2-16-11-16-2-6-9

3-11-16-6-7  14-19-14-6-9

18-2-11-8  17-19-4-6-7-9

1-19-4-2-9-11-5-7  26-2-4-6-9

16-5-7-4-19-14-9

18-11-10-6-9

9-5-26-3-11-23  16-7-11-19-4-9

Answer on page 49.

# RIDDLING REPTILES

In each group, which one is the reptile?

**1.**
caiman   con man   keyman

**2.**
asterisk   basilisk   burdocks

**3.**
anaconda   analogy   antipasto

**4.**
plink   skink   clink

**5.**
gingko   gecko   gable

**6.**
cleft   drift   swift

**7.**
proton   python   protein

**8.**
comedian   cotillion   chameleon

**9.**
viper   vapor   valor

**10.**
kickback   leatherback   greenback

Answer on page 49.

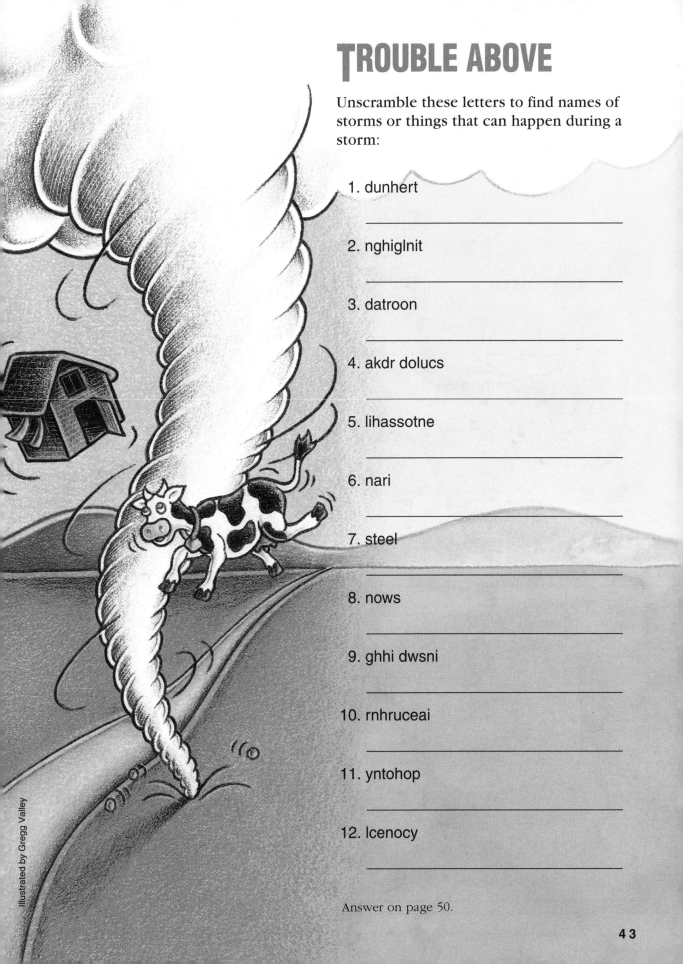

# TROUBLE ABOVE

Unscramble these letters to find names of storms or things that can happen during a storm:

1. dunhert

_____

2. nghiglnit

_____

3. datroon

_____

4. akdr dolucs

_____

5. lihassotne

_____

6. nari

_____

7. steel

_____

8. nows

_____

9. ghhi dwsni

_____

10. rnhruceai

_____

11. yntohop

_____

12. lcenocy

_____

Answer on page 50.

Illustrated by Gregg Valley

# FURNITURE FUN

The four rooms on the right have all been rearranged and the furniture changed around. Can you match the rooms on the right with the correct ones on the left? No furniture has been added or taken away.

Illustrated by John Nez

Answer on page 50.

# S IS FOR SUPERHERO!

Aside from the superhero, there are at least 30 other objects in this picture that begin with the letter "S." How many can you find?

# ANSWERS

**SETTING SAIL** (page 3)

| | |
|---|---|
| 1 | 5 |
| 6 | 2 |
| 4 | 3 |

**COMMON SENSE** (pages 4-5)

1- They all fly.
2- Horns
3- Points
4- Costumes
5- Handles
6- Names begin with "B"
7- All come in pairs
8- Tongues
9- Strings
10- They all have leaves.
11- Lines

**BAFFLING BOXES** (page 7)

**THE CLEAN-UP BRIGADE** (pages 8-9)

Well groomed!

**MULTIPLYING RABBITS** (page 10)

1- Thumper
2- Rabbit
3- March Hare
4- Easter Bunny
5-Peter Rabbit
6-Bugs Bunny
7-Brer Rabbit
8-Roger Rabbit

**MAILBOX MEMORIES** (page 12)

1. Purpletown, Pennsylvania
2. Purpletown Times
3. M
4. A heart
5. Red
6. Three
7. Three (dog, frog, ladybug)
8. She was mailing a letter to Ohio.
9. No
10. One

**SHE SAVES SEASHELLS** (page 12)

Only four months (May, June, July, August) don't have "R" in their names. In those months, she will collect a total of 123 shells.

**DOT MAGIC** (page 13)

Taj Mahal

**WORD PAIRS** (page 16)

1. truck, car
2. cat, dog
3. can, jar
4. arm, leg
5. itch, burn
6. old, age
7. bad, good
8. in, out
9. his, her
10. crib, bed
11. farm, ranch
12. run, fast

## LAST GAS (page 17)

Mr. Vickers drove the van (4). He did not stop for oil (4), water (3,5), to use the bathroom (3), or for air (2). He stopped for gas. Either Stuart or the driver of the motorcycle stopped for water (3). Either Taylor or Zuna stopped for water (5). Zuna did not drive the motorcycle (3), so Taylor is the driver of the motorcycle. Since only one person stopped for water, Taylor is the person who did so. By elimination, Zuna drove the semi (5), and Ms. Stuart stopped to use the bathroom (3). Zuna did not stop for air (2); he stopped to buy oil. Ms. Stuart was not driving the station wagon (2); she drove the sedan. By elimination, Mr. Wells was the driver of the station wagon. He stopped to put air in a tire.

In Summary:
Stuart, sedan, bathroom
Taylor, motorcycle, water
Vickers, van, gas
Wells, station wagon, air
Zuna, semi-truck, oil

## IN THE KITCHEN (pages 18-19)

## ROW, ROW, ROW (page 20)

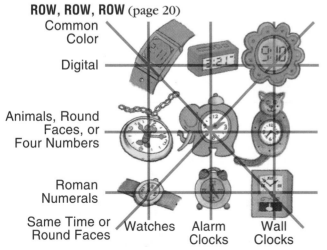

Common Color
Digital
Animals, Round Faces, or Four Numbers
Roman Numerals
Same Time or Round Faces
Watches
Alarm Clocks
Wall Clocks

## STOP, LOOK, AND LIST (page 21)

These are the answers we found. You may have found others.

| THINGS IN A POOL | HOT WORDS |
|---|---|
| Float | Flame |
| Filter | Fry |
| Fins | Fire |

| THINGS TO EAT | NUMBERS |
|---|---|
| Frankfurter | Four |
| Food | Fourteen |
| French Fries | Forty |

## PICTURE MIXER (pages 22-23)

## TALL TALE TOOLS (page 24)

Johnny Appleseed - Shovel
Pecos Bill - Lariat
Paul Bunyan - Ax
Mike Fink - Fishing Pole
John Henry - Hammer
Casey Jones - Wrench

## WHAT'S IN A WORD? (page 25)

These are the answers we found. You may have found others.

emir, emit, gem, gent, germ, get, grim, grime, grin, grip, gripe, grist, grit, imp, imprint, inert, ingest, insert, inspire, inter, ire, iris, men, merit, Mets, mine, miner, mini, mint, mire, miser, mist, mister, mite, miter, nest, net, peg, pen, pest, pet, pie, pig, pin, pine, pint, pit, priest, prim, prime, print, rein, remit, rent, resign, rest, ring, rip, ripe, ripen, rise, risen, sent, sign, sin, sine, sing, singe, singer, sip, sir, sire, siren, sit, site, spent, spin, spine, spire, spirit, spit, spite, spring, sprint, sprite, stein, stem, step, stern, sting, stinger, stir, string, strip, stripe, ten, term, tern, tie, tiger, time, timer, tin, tine, tinge, tip, tire, tries, trim, trip, tripe

## MONKEYING AROUND (pages 26-27)

Crossword solution with answers: SAPAJOU, GOLDEN LION, SPIDER, GORILLA, LEMUR, ORANGUTAN, RED UAKARI, AYE AYE, MARMOSET, MACAQUE, RHESUS, POTTO, MANDRILL, BLACK, SHREW, SAKI, MONKEY

## INSTANT PICTURES (page 29)

## GLOBE PROBE (pages 30-31)
This answer appears on page 50.

## TROUBLE ON THE LINE (page 33)
A. Truck
B. Camera
C. Video Game
D. Computer

## DAZE OF THE MONTH (pages 34-35)
Why are Saturday and Sunday so limp?
They're the week ends. (weak)

## ORDER IN THE COIN ROOM (pages 36-37)
1. Value from least to most
2. Size from smallest to largest
3. Alphabetical order by name of coin
4. Weight from heaviest to lightest
5. By date from newest to oldest
6. Alphabetical order by person on coin
7. Coins in order from thickest to thinnest

## BIG AL (page 38)
1. real
2. seal
3. deal
4. steal
5. petal
6. coral
7. moral
8. mammal
9. mental
10. cereal
11. aerial
12. several
13. cardinal
14. autumnal

## WONDERS DOWN UNDER (pages 40-41)
OLD DOG BONES
WORMS
PEANUTS
BURIED TREASURE
MOLES
FOSSILS
ANT COLONIES
POTATOES
WATER PIPES
COAL MINERS
DINOSAUR BONES
TURNIPS
CAVES
SUBWAY TRAINS

## RIDDLING REPTILES (page 42)
1. caiman (a South American relative of the alligator)
2. basilisk (a Central American lizard)
3. anaconda (a South American snake)
4. skink (a long-tailed lizard)
5. gecko (a padded-foot lizard)
6. swift (also known as "fence lizard")
7. python (a tropical snake)
8. chameleon (a lizard that changes colors)
9. viper (a venomous snake)
10. leatherback (a large sea turtle)

## TROUBLE ABOVE (page 43)

1. thunder
2. lightning
3. tornado
4. dark clouds
5. hailstones
6. rain
7. sleet
8. snow
9. high winds
10. hurricane
11. typhoon
12. cyclone

## FURNITURE FUN (pages 44-45)

1 - C
2 - A
3 - D
4 - B.

## GLOBE PROBE (pages 30-31)

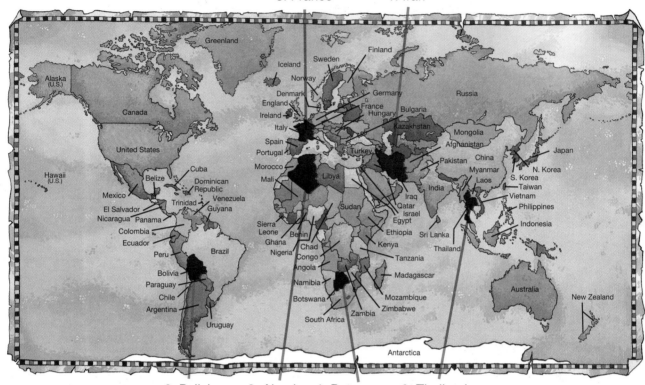

5. France
1. Iran
2. Bolivia
3. Algeria
4. Botswana
6. Thailand